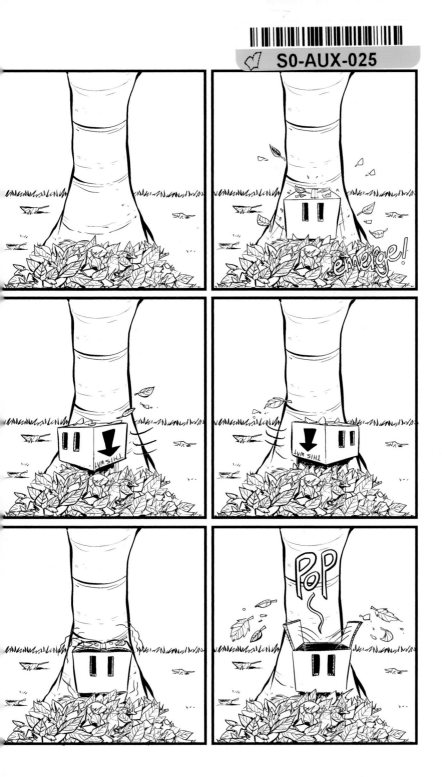

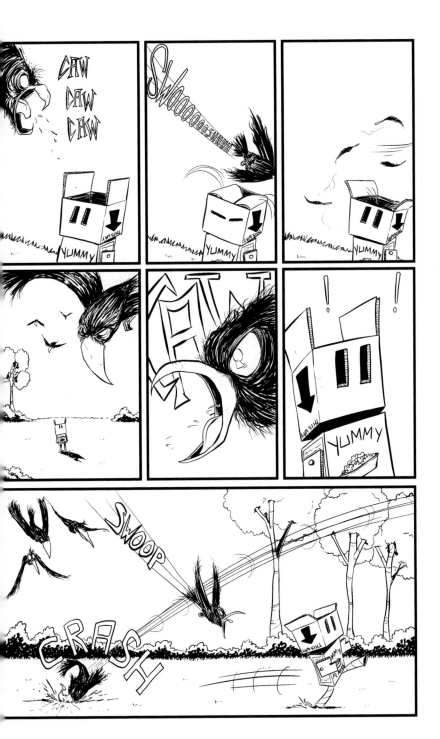

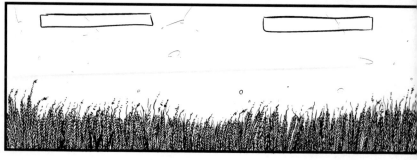

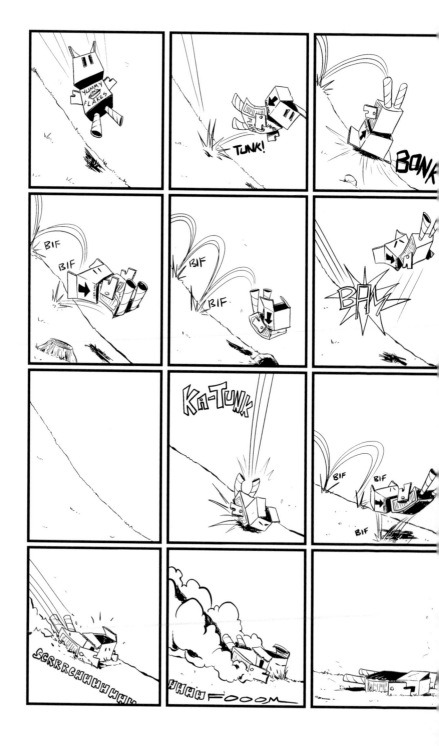

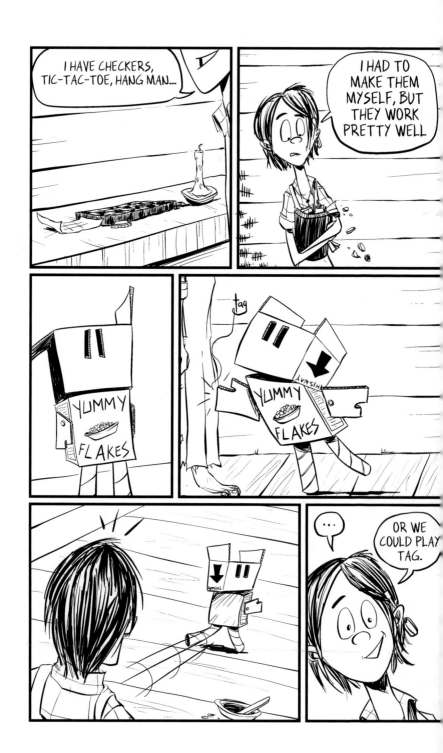

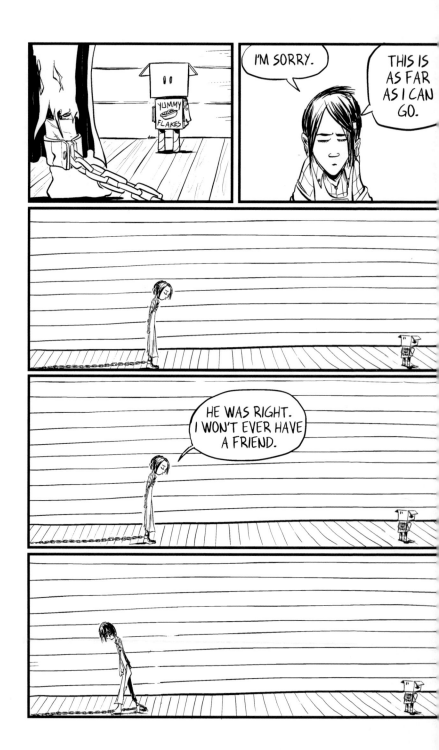

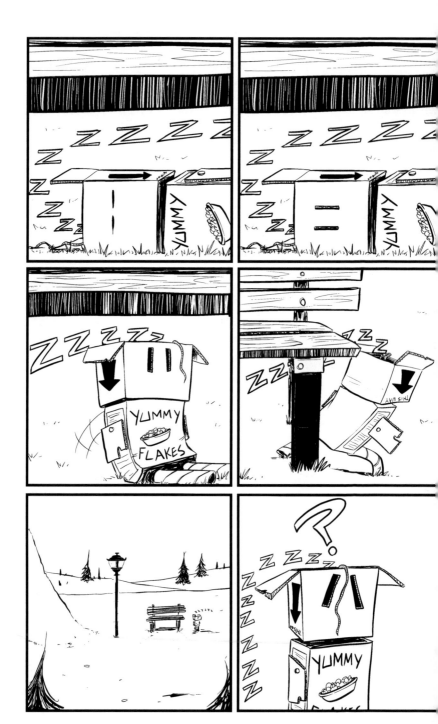

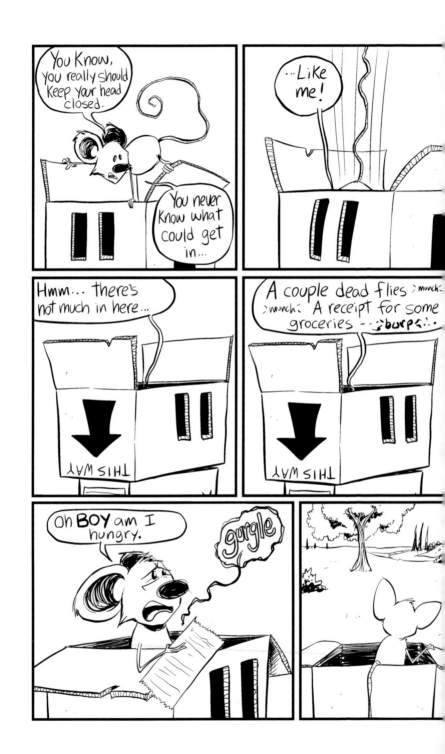

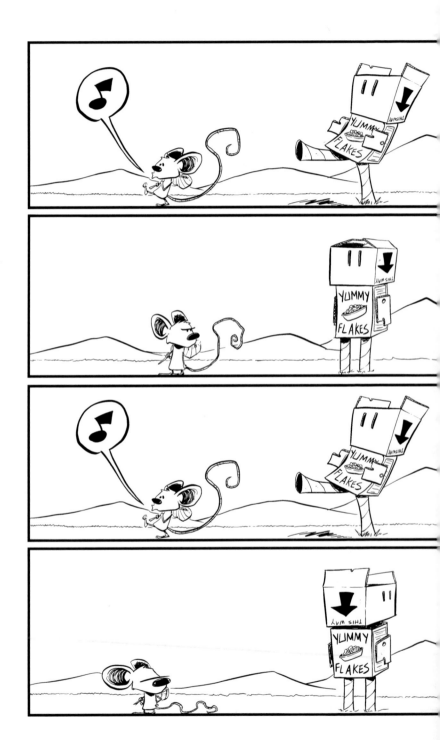

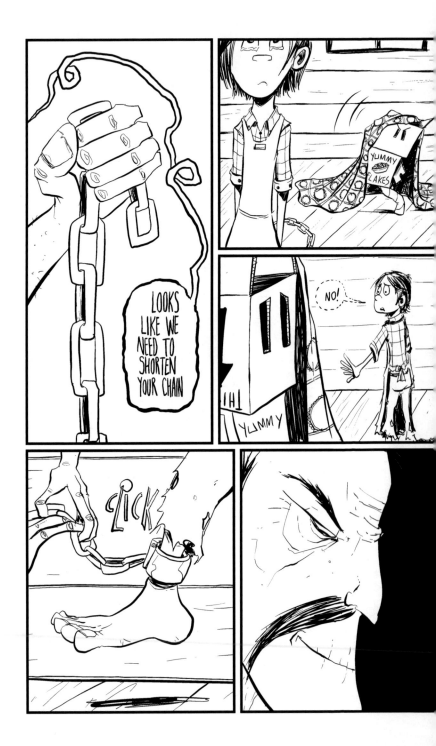

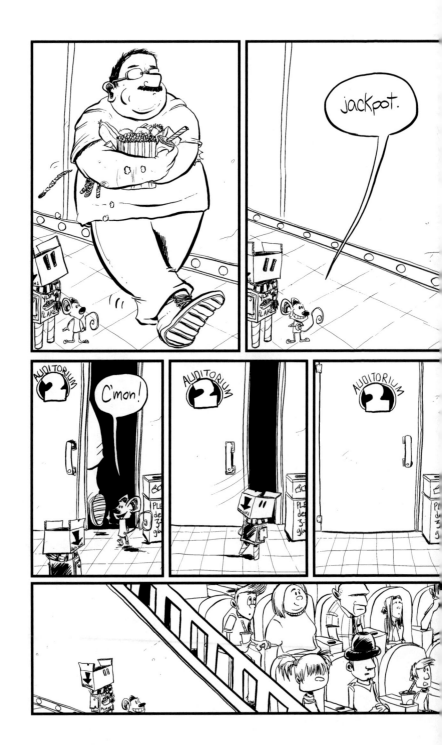

That's quite a sight.

Though not as entertaining as the ROCKET RAT t.v. series!

Did you ever see it?

Years ago, I used to be a pet.

A boy named George found me one day and took me home.

He kept me in his pocket and fed me bits of cheese he'd sneak from the fridge when his Mom wasn't looking.

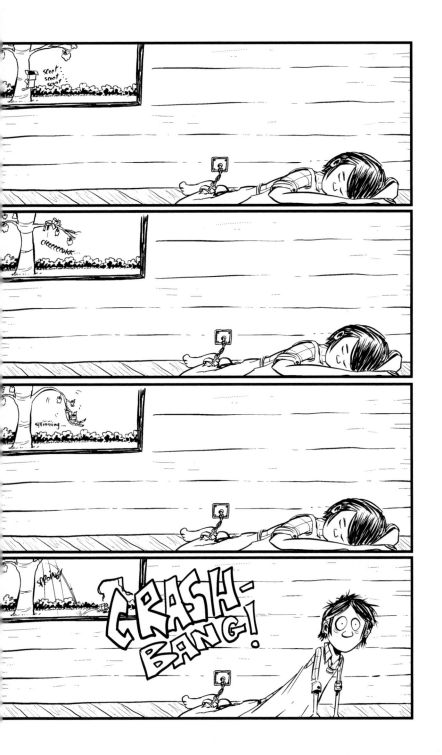

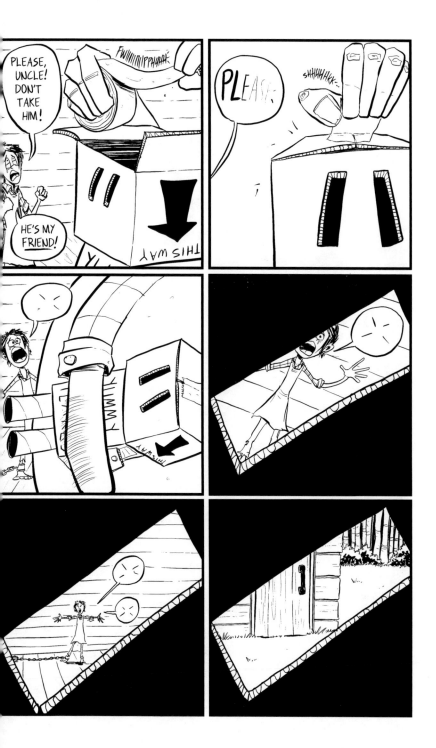

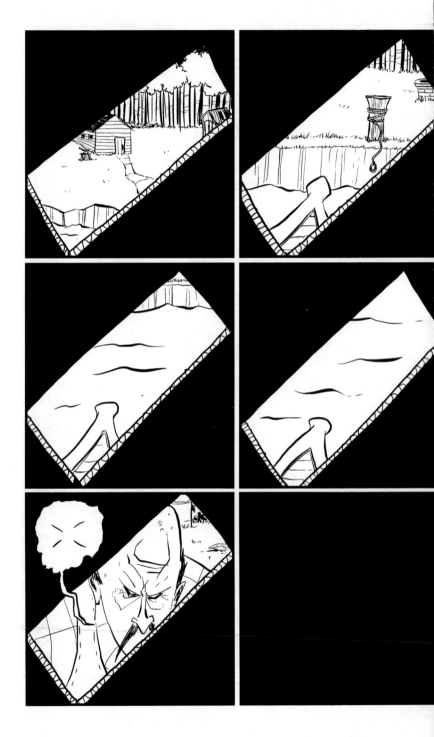

You know this place, don't you?

Is this home?

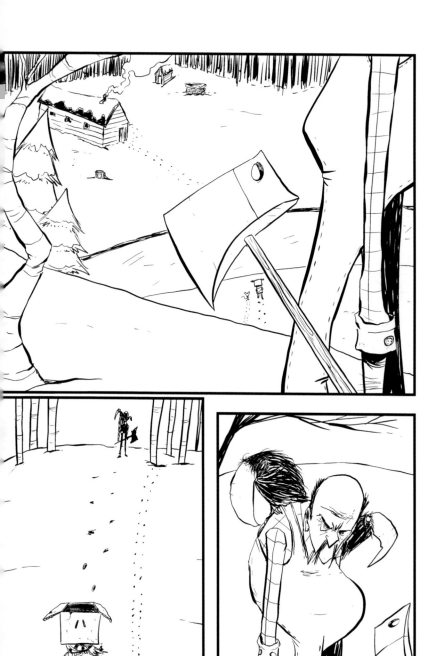

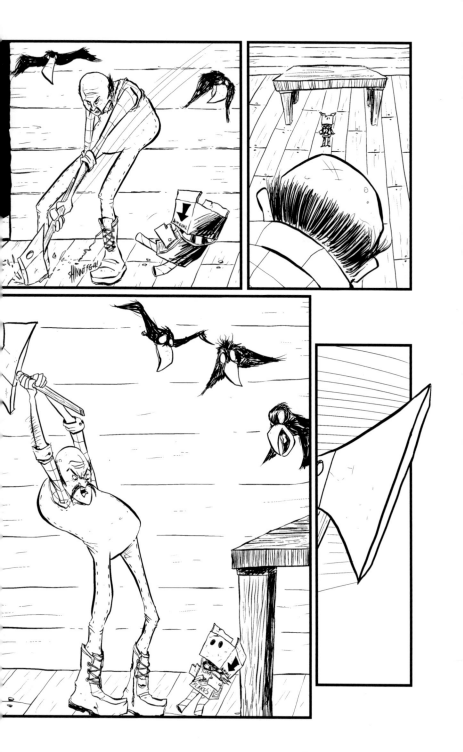

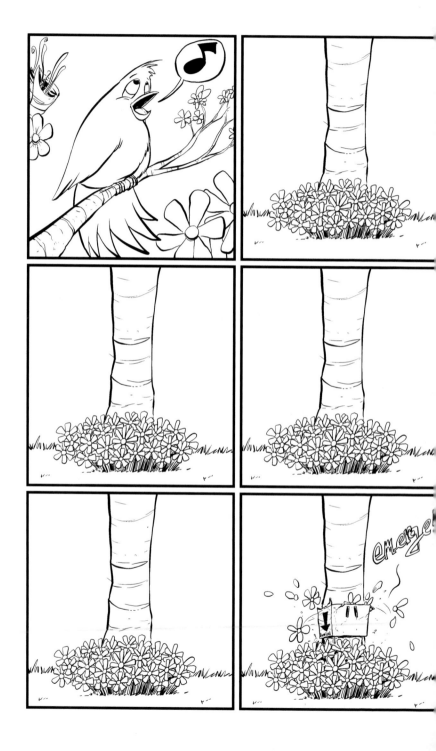

The End.